It's Elementary!

230 Math Word Problems

Book A

M. J. Owen

EDUCATORS PUBLISHING SERVICE
Cambridge and Toronto

To my favorite young mathematician, Ellie. May solving problems always be fun for you. I love you.

Design by Joyce C. Weston
Illustrations by Tatjana Mai-Wyss

Printed in the U.S.A.
ISBN 0-8388-2409-9
978-0-8388-2409-2
3 4 5 6 7 PAH 11 10 09 08 07

Contents

To the Teacher

Many elementary age students have difficulty solving word problems. In my classroom I have found two primary reasons for this difficulty. First they attempt to solve problems too quickly, and second, they fail to visualize the problem and note key words so they select the wrong operation. The following word problem approach has been one I have used with great success.

In my classroom students break down problems in the following way: (1) they look for key words in the problem, circle the key word, and put the operation sign in the THOUGHT (T) line; (2) students put INFORMATION (I) down. Students form their NUMBER SENTENCE (N) and fill in their SOLUTION SENTENCE (S). I have provided an example below. I hope the exercises in this book will provide an opportunity for word problem fun and success. Happy problem solving!

Example: The drum major has 7 gold buttons on his uniform. The trumpet player has 8 silver buttons on her uniform. How many buttons do the drum major and the trumpet player have altogether?

Thought (T): _____ + _____

Information (I): _____ 7 gold buttons, _____
_____ 8 silver buttons _____

Number Sentence (N): _____ 7 + 8 = _____

Solution Sentence (S): _____ The drum major _____
_____ and the trumpet player have _____
_____ 15 buttons altogether. _____

WORK SPACE

Solving Addition Word Problems with TINS

When you are reading a word problem, think of yourself as a trailblazer. Key words can give you directions to the correct checkpoints. Here are some addition key words.

🔑 in all   🔑 altogether
🔑 sum   🔑 total

You may want to add other addition words you know to this list.

When you see an addition key word in a problem, circle it and write + above the key word. Then write + on the THOUGHT line. Next, circle and write down the important INFORMATION from the word problem. Sometimes it helps to draw a picture of the important information. It's also a good idea to cross out information that doesn't seem important to the problem. Now write your information as a NUMBER SENTENCE. Then plug your answer into your SOLUTION SENTENCE.

Remember to check your work.

Please examine the sample problem below.

Example: According to Hans Christian Andersen one fussy princess slept on (20 mattresses) and (20 featherbeds.) One pea was placed between 2 of the mattresses. How many (mattresses) and (featherbeds) did the fussy princess rest on (in all?)

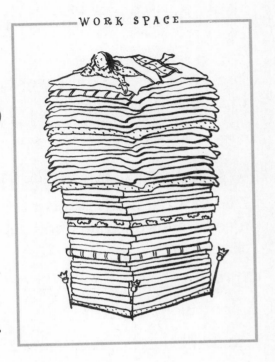

WORK SPACE

Thought: __+_____

Information: __20 mattresses,__

__20 featherbeds__

Number Sentence: ____20 + 20 =____

Solution Sentence: __There were 40__

__mattresses and featherbeds in all.__

A good way to remember how to solve word problems is to think of the word *TINS*.

T	=	Thought
I	=	Information
N	=	Number Sentence
S	=	Solution Sentence

Good luck and happy problem solving!

Try It Out

Use TINS to solve these word problems. Remember to circle key words and draw pictures. Have fun!

---

1. Marcy went to the store and bought 7 erasers. Her brother bought 3 erasers. How many erasers did Marcy and her brother have altogether?

Thought: _____

Information: _____

_____

Number Sentence: _____

Solution Sentence: _____

_____

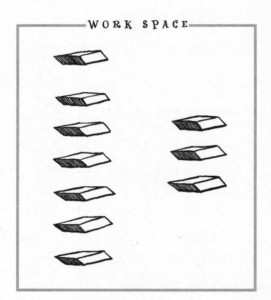

WORK SPACE

---

2. Mrs. Cavazos traveled to the mall. She bought two new red T-shirts and three new blue T-shirts. How many T-shirts did Mrs. Cavazos buy in all?

Thought: _____

Information: _____

_____

Number Sentence: _____

Solution Sentence: _____

_____

WORK SPACE

3. Gregory has four dogs, three cats, and two birds. How many dogs and birds does Gregory have in all?

WORK SPACE

Thought: _____

Information: _____

_____

Number Sentence: _____

Solution Sentence: _____

_____

4. Samantha and Piper both love to read! Samantha read 4 books over the weekend and Piper read 9 books over the weekend. What was the total number of books that the girls read?

WORK SPACE

Thought: _____

Information: _____

_____

Number Sentence: _____

Solution Sentence: _____

_____

5. Mrs. Dunn has five sons. She buys a jug of milk on Monday, two jugs of milk on Wednesday and four jugs of milk on Friday. How many jugs of milk did Mrs. Dunn buy in all three days?

Thought: _____

Information: _____

_____

Number Sentence: _____

Solution Sentence: _____

_____

WORK SPACE

6. Sasha scored three goals at her soccer game on Saturday and one goal at her soccer game on Sunday. How many goals did Sasha score over the weekend?

Thought: _____

Information: _____

_____

Number Sentence: _____

Solution Sentence: _____

_____

WORK SPACE

7. Leanne has two brothers and three sisters. How many brothers and sisters does Leanne have altogether?

WORK SPACE

Thought: _____

Information: _____

_____

Number Sentence: _____

Solution Sentence: _____

_____

8. Marty likes to ride her bike. She rode her bike two miles on Tuesday and four miles on Thursday. What was the total number of miles Marty rode her bike on Tuesday and Thursday?

WORK SPACE

Thought: _____

Information: _____

_____

Number Sentence: _____

Solution Sentence: _____

_____

9. Waldo the waiter sold 12 gift certificates over the holidays. Last year he sold 8 certificates. How many gift certificates has Waldo sold altogether?

Thought: _____

Information: _____

_____

Number Sentence: _____

Solution Sentence: _____

_____

WORK SPACE

10. After drafting the Declaration of Independence, Ben Franklin and Thomas Jefferson signed this document along with 54 other colonists. How many people in all signed the Declaration of Independence?

Thought: _____

Information: _____

_____

Number Sentence: _____

Solution Sentence: _____

_____

WORK SPACE

Solving Subtraction Word Problems with TINS

You can use TINS to solve subtraction word problems, too! Uncharted territory can cause you to stumble off course. Remember to follow the right path.

0—⊶ left

0—⊶ subtract

0—⊶ difference

0—⊶ how many more

0—⊶ how much more

Can you think of any other subtraction key words? If so, add them to the list.

When you see a subtraction key word in a problem, circle it and write – above the key word. Then write – on the THOUGHT line. Next, circle and write down the important INFORMATION from the word problem. Sometimes it helps to draw a picture of the important information from the word problem. It's also a good idea to cross out extra information that doesn't seem important to the problem. Now write your information as a NUMBER SENTENCE. Then plug your answer into your SOLUTION SENTENCE.

Example: A goliath frog of West Africa is (32 inches long.) Buster's frog, Splash, is only (4 inches long.) Find the (difference) in inches between Buster's frog and the goliath frog.

Thought: _— _____

Information: _goliath frog is 32 inches,_
_____Splash is 4 inches_____

Number Sentence: _____32 – 4 =_____

Solution Sentence: _A goliath frog is 28_
inches longer than Splash.

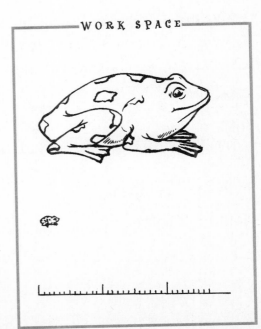

WORK SPACE

Try It Out

Use TINS to solve these word problems. Remember to circle key words and draw pictures. Remember to read each solution sentence to make sure it makes sense!

---

1. A marine crab has 10 legs. Only 2 of the crab's legs have large claws. How many of the crab's legs do not have large claws?

Thought: _____

Information: _____

_____

Number Sentence: _____

Solution Sentence: _____

_____

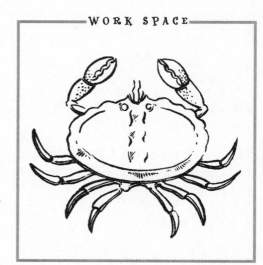

WORK SPACE

---

2. Sitting in a circle on chairs in Cecilia's backyard, 12 friends played musical chairs. Cecilia took away 3 chairs. How many lawn chairs were left for Cecilia's friends?

Thought: _____

Information: _____

_____

Number Sentence: _____

Solution Sentence: _____

_____

WORK SPACE

3. There are twenty-eight days in the month of February. It snowed on seventeen days during February and did not snow the remaining days. How many days during February did it not snow?

T: _____

I: _____

_____

N: _____

S: _____

_____

WORK SPACE

February

---

4. Suzanne ordered eleven books from the October book club. Three of the books are for her younger sister. How many books did Suzanne order for herself?

T: _____

I: _____

_____

N: _____

S: _____

_____

WORK SPACE

5. Molly earns $12 a week for her allowance. Andrew earns $9 a week for allowance. How much more money does Molly earn each week?

T: _____

I: _____

_____

N: _____

S: _____

_____

WORK SPACE

6. Carlotta has 9 dimes. Rollo has 3 dimes. How many more dimes does Carlotta have?

T: _____

I: _____

_____

N: _____

S: _____

_____

WORK SPACE

7. Claire is keeping a diary. The diary has twenty pages. Claire has written on ten pages. How many pages does Claire have left to write on?

T: _____

I: _____

_____

N: _____

S: _____

_____

WORK SPACE

8. Bianca invited six friends to her house for a slumber party. Two of her friends could not come. How many of Bianca's friends came to her party?

T: _____

I: _____

_____

N: _____

S: _____

_____

WORK SPACE

9. Audrey jogs three times a week. She jogs three miles on Monday, five miles on Wednesday and four miles on Friday. How many more miles does Audrey jog on Wednesday than on Friday?

T: _____

I: _____

_____

N: _____

S: _____

_____

WORK SPACE

10. Wesley lives seven blocks from the neighborhood park. Cameron lives nineteen blocks from the same park. How many blocks closer does Wesley live to the neighborhood park?

T: _____

I: _____

_____

N: _____

S: _____

_____

WORK SPACE

Addition and Subtraction Mixed Practice

Draw a picture, circle key words, and use TINS to solve these problems. Don't forget to cross out extra information!

---

1. The African butterfly has a wingspan of 11 inches. A Pacific swallowtail butterfly's wingspan is 10 inches. Find the difference in inches between the 2 butterflies.

Thought: _____

Information: _____

_____

Number Sentence: _____

Solution Sentence: _____

_____

WORK SPACE

---

2. Elizabeth has forty-seven stickers in her sticker collection. Martha has twenty-eight stickers in her sticker collection. How many more stickers does Elizabeth have in her collection?

Thought: _____

Information: _____

_____

Number Sentence: _____

Solution Sentence: _____

_____

WORK SPACE

3. Gwen is reading a novel by her favorite author. She reads seventeen pages Thursday, twenty-eight pages Friday, and forty-nine pages Saturday. What is the total number of pages that Gwen reads?

Thought: _____

Information: _____

_____

Number Sentence: _____

Solution Sentence: _____

_____

WORK SPACE

4. Sleeping Beauty slept for 100 years. Rip Van Wrinkle was reported to have slept for 20 years. How many more years did Sleeping Beauty sleep?

Thought: _____

Information: _____

_____

Number Sentence: _____

Solution Sentence: _____

_____

WORK SPACE

5. Marissa's summer school class will take fifteen field trips during summer school. The class will ride the bus for twelve of the field trips and take the subway for the other field trips. How many field trips will Marissa's class take where they need to use the subway?

WORK SPACE

Thought: _____

Information: _____

_____

Number Sentence: _____

Solution Sentence: _____

_____

6. The Simmons Elementary School PTA bought 134 school T-shirts to sell to students. They sold a total of 74 T-shirts before spring break. How many T-shirts does the PTA have left to sell?

WORK SPACE

T: _____

I: _____

_____

N: _____

S: _____

_____

7. On a hot summer day Ruby decides to walk to the beach with her sister. She will walk four miles to the beach, two miles once she arrives at the beach, and then an additional four miles to return back home. How many miles will Ruby expect to walk in all?

T: _____

I: _____

_____

N: _____

S: _____

_____

WORK SPACE

8. Sarah Lee is recording music on a compact disc. There is enough space on the CD for her to record 32 songs. Sarah Lee has already recorded 18 songs. How many more songs can Sarah Lee record on the CD?

T: _____

I: _____

_____

N: _____

S: _____

_____

WORK SPACE

9. Jake and Jonah sell lemonade. They sold 56 glasses on Friday and 69 glasses on Saturday. How many more glasses did the boys sell on Saturday?

T: _____

I: _____

_____

N: _____

S: _____

_____

WORK SPACE

10. The Declaration of Independence was signed in 1776. How old will the Declaration of Independence be in the year 2006?

T: _____

I: _____

_____

N: _____

S: _____

_____

WORK SPACE

11. European penguins of Antarctica are 36 inches tall. Blue penguins of Australia are 20 inches tall. Find the difference in height between the 2 penguins.

T: _____

I: _____

_____

N: _____

S: _____

_____

WORK SPACE

---

12. Margery signed up for a pottery class at the art school near her house. During her six-week art class she made three bowls and two mugs. How many pieces of pottery did Margery make in all?

T: _____

I: _____

_____

N: _____

S: _____

_____

WORK SPACE

13. Lindsey loves milk shakes! During summer vacation she drank 32 strawberry milkshakes, 44 banana milkshakes, and 39 chocolate milkshakes. How many more chocolate milkshakes did Lindsey drink than strawberry milkshakes?

T: _____

I: _____

_____

N: _____

S: _____

_____

WORK SPACE

14. Over the weekend Peter ran in 2 road races. On Saturday he ran in a race that was 3 miles and on Sunday he ran in a race that was 10 miles. How many miles did Peter run over the weekend in all?

T: _____

I: _____

_____

N: _____

S: _____

_____

WORK SPACE

15. Savannah put birdseed and 2 bird feeders in her yard. During one week of bird watching she reported seeing 34 blue jays and 52 cardinals. How many more cardinals did Savannah report seeing?

T: _____

I: _____

_____

N: _____

S: _____

_____

WORK SPACE

16. Joanna is making jewelry to earn extra money. She makes 14 bracelets, 13 necklaces, and 15 anklets. How many bracelets and anklets does Joanna make altogether?

T: _____

I: _____

_____

N: _____

S: _____

_____

WORK SPACE

17. Mr. and Mrs. Nice are going to a family carnival. They plan to take their five children, three friends, and two of their neighbors. What is the total number of people Mr. and Mrs. Nice are planning on taking to the carnival?

T: _____

I: _____

_____

N: _____

S: _____

_____

WORK SPACE

18. Of the 25 highest mountains in the world, 19 are in the Himalayas. How many of these mountains are found in other parts of the world?

T: _____

I: _____

_____

N: _____

S: _____

_____

WORK SPACE

19. There are seventeen students in Ms. Hannon's second grade class. Four of the students play on a baseball team. How many of Ms. Hannon's students do not play on a baseball team?

T: _____

I: _____

_____

N: _____

S: _____

_____

WORK SPACE

20. Lane collects mugs from different places that he visits. He collected 29 mugs when he traveled around the United States and 14 mugs when he traveled around Mexico. How many mugs did Lane collect in all?

T: _____

I: _____

_____

N: _____

S: _____

_____

WORK SPACE

21. Mr. Levine's class challenged Mrs. Kreuts's class to a one week Read-A-Thon. During the week Mr. Levine's class read a total of 141 books. Mrs. Kreuts's class read 156 books. How many books did the two classes read in all?

T: _____

I: _____

_____

N: _____

S: _____

_____

WORK SPACE

22. Gladys knows that there are 365 days in 1 year. She read that for 186 days each year the sun does not shine at the North Pole. How many days will Gladys report that the sun will shine at the North Pole in 1 year?

T: _____

I: _____

_____

N: _____

S: _____

_____

WORK SPACE

23. Montana picked daisies from her friend's garden. She picked 14 daisies on Monday, 15 on Wednesday, and 17 on Friday. How many daisies did Montana pick in all?

T: _____

I: _____

_____

N: _____

S: _____

_____

WORK SPACE

24. Mac is building a patio in his backyard. He plans to use 57 red bricks and 61 gray bricks when he builds his patio. What is the total number of bricks that Mac plans to use when he builds his patio?

T: _____

I: _____

_____

N: _____

S: _____

_____

WORK SPACE

Addition and Subtraction: Write Your Own I

Try writing your own addition and subtraction word problems. Make a question out of the information provided and then use TINS to solve the problems. Challenge your friends to solve the problems you create.

Example: Phoebe has $17. She spent $6.

Question: Phoebe has $17. She spent $6 on a new headband. How much money does Phoebe have left?

Thought: −

Information: has $17, spent $6

Number Sentence: 17 − 6 =

Solution Sentence: Phoebe has $11 now.

WORK SPACE

17
-6
11

---

1. Lucy has six bananas. She eats four bananas.

Question: _____

_____

_____ ?

Thought: _____

Information: _____

_____

Number Sentence: _____

Solution Sentence: _____

WORK SPACE

2. Betty has 4 goldfish. Maria has 7 goldfish.

Question: _____

_____

_____?

Thought: _____

Information: _____

_____

Number Sentence: _____

Solution Sentence: _____

_____

WORK SPACE

3. Belinda has 27 kites. She gives away 13 kites.

Question: _____

_____

_____?

T: _____

I: _____

_____

N: _____

S: _____

_____

WORK SPACE

Addition and Subtraction: Write Your Own II

Write your own addition or subtraction word problems. Then use TINS to solve them. Remember to draw a picture, circle key words, and cross out information that isn't important. Happy problem writing!

1. _____

_____

_____?

Thought: _____

Information: _____

_____

Number Sentence: _____

Solution Sentence: _____

_____

WORK SPACE

2. _____

_____

_____?

Thought: _____

Information: _____

_____

Number Sentence: _____

Solution Sentence: _____

_____

WORK SPACE

3. _____

_____

_____ ?

T: _____

I: _____

_____

N: _____

S: _____

_____

WORK SPACE

4. _____

_____

_____ ?

T: _____

I: _____

_____

N: _____

S: _____

_____

WORK SPACE

5. _____

_____

_____ ?

T: _____

I: _____

_____

N: _____

S: _____

_____

WORK SPACE

Addition and Subtraction: More Mixed Practice

Please draw a picture, circle key words, and use TINS to solve the following word problems. Be careful and remember what TINS stands for.

T	=	Thought
I	=	Information
N	=	Number Sentence
S	=	Solution Sentence

Good Luck!

---

1. Savannah has 19 hair ribbons in a treasure box in her room. Her mother fixes her hair in pigtails and uses 5 hair ribbons. How many hair ribbons are left in the treasure box?

Thought: _____

Information: _____

_____

Number Sentence: _____

Solution Sentence: _____

_____

WORK SPACE

2. The Bumstead boys have 2 official baseballs. Each baseball weighs 5 ounces. How many ounces do their baseballs weigh altogether?

Thought: _____

Information: _____

_____

Number Sentence: _____

Solution Sentence: _____

_____

WORK SPACE

3. Trudy weaves yarn together to make bracelets for her friends. She made 9 purple bracelets, 5 yellow bracelets and 4 orange bracelets. She gave away 5 purple bracelets and decides to save the rest for holiday gifts. How many purple bracelets does Trudy have left?

T: _____

I: _____

_____

N: _____

S: _____

_____

WORK SPACE

4. Desiree's family is traveling to her grandma's house in another state. They travel 102 miles on Monday and 95 miles on Tuesday before they arrive at Grandma's house. How many more miles did Desiree's family travel on Monday?

T: _____

I: _____

_____

N: _____

S: _____

_____

WORK SPACE

5. Jason wrote a report about whales. He wrote 11 pages on Thursday and 12 pages on Saturday. How many pages is Jason's report in all?

T: _____

I: _____

_____

N: _____

S: _____

_____

WORK SPACE

6. There are two classes of second graders at DePaul Elementary. Mrs. Baumann's class has 18 students and Mr. Malloy's class has 21 students. How many students do the 2 teachers have altogether?

T: _____

I: _____

_____

N: _____

S: _____

_____

WORK SPACE

7. The second grade class at Bryker Heights is putting on a play to celebrate the holidays. They sell 129 tickets for their first performance and 104 tickets for their second performance. How many more tickets did the second grade class sell for their first performance?

T: _____

I: _____

_____

N: _____

S: _____

_____

8. Betsy and Melinda will be paid $1 a window to wash the windows at Mr. Macaroo's grocery store. The girls wash 8 windows in the morning and 7 windows in the afternoon. How many windows did the girls wash in all?

T: _____

I: _____

_____

N: _____

S: _____

_____

WORK SPACE

9. Terrance is training for field day. He ran 32 minutes Saturday, 27 minutes Sunday, and 37 minutes Tuesday. How many more minutes did Terrance run on Tuesday than he ran on Sunday?

T: _____

I: _____

_____

N: _____

S: _____

_____

WORK SPACE

10. Theresa's family is going on vacation. Theresa saves $41 to spend on souvenirs during vacation and her brother saves $34. How much more money did Theresa save?

T: _____

I: _____

_____

N: _____

S: _____

_____

WORK SPACE

---

11. Carl's Cards sold 76 baseball cards during the first weekend in October and 58 baseball cards during the second weekend of October. How many more baseball cards did Carl's Cards sell during the first weekend of October?

T: _____

I: _____

_____

N: _____

S: _____

_____

WORK SPACE

12. Spiders have 8 legs and 2 parts to their body. Ben has collected 2 spiders for his science experiment. How many legs are on Ben's spiders altogether?

T: _____

I: _____

_____

N: _____

S: _____

_____

WORK SPACE

---

13. Peter's Scout troop took three hikes while they were camping out in Colorado. They hiked 11 miles on the first day, 8 miles on the second day, and 5 miles on the third day. What was the total number of miles Peter's Scout troop hiked?

T: _____

I: _____

_____

N: _____

S: _____

_____

WORK SPACE

14. Mrs. Weinstein signed her daughter up for art lessons. The lessons cost $55 for six months and the supplies cost $10. What was the total amount Mrs. Weinstein spent on art class and supplies?

WORK SPACE

T: _____

I: _____

_____

N: _____

S: _____

_____

15. While Sandra was away at camp she sent her family 17 letters and 6 packages. How many more letters did Sandra send her family?

WORK SPACE

T: _____

I: _____

_____

N: _____

S: _____

_____

16. Penelope's puppy dog gained 5 pounds in October, 3 pounds in November, and 4 pounds in December. How many pounds did her puppy gain during all three months?

T: _____

I: _____

_____

N: _____

S: _____

_____

WORK SPACE

17. During the week Sally spends 2 hours on the computer on Tuesday, 1 hour on Wednesday, and 3 hours on Friday. How many hours will Sally spend on the computer in all?

T: _____

I: _____

_____

N: _____

S: _____

_____

WORK SPACE

18. Janna and Marla both took pictures while visiting a museum during a school field trip. Janna took 94 pictures and Marla took 88 pictures. How many more pictures did Janna take?

T: _____

I: _____

_____

N: _____

S: _____

_____

WORK SPACE

19. Andrea counts the total number of blocks she walks to school and then from school to the post office. She walks 9 blocks to school and 2 blocks to the post office. How many blocks does Andrea walk altogether?

T: _____

I: _____

_____

N: _____

S: _____

_____

WORK SPACE

20. During the summer months there were 54 sunny days, 32 rainy days, and 11 cloudy days without rain. What is the total number of days when no rain fell during the summer?

T: _____

I: _____

_____

N: _____

S: _____

_____

WORK SPACE

Addition and Subtraction: Explain

Use TINS to solve each word problem. Then write at least 2 sentences explaining how you solved the problem. An example has been provided to help you.

Example: Jodie received (2 new hats) for her collection. She already had (7 hats.) How many hats has she (in all?)
+

Thought: _____ + _____

Information: ___2 new hats, 7 old hats___

Number Sentence: ___2 + 7 =___

Solution Sentence: ___Jodie has 9 hats in all.___

Explain: ___I add the number of hats___
___together because the question___
___asks for how many "in all." A___
___person who collects hats could___
___have 9 hats.___

WORK SPACE

1. Mr. Giles is taking a ten-hour flight to Europe. During the trip he is awake for two hours. How many hours did Mr. Giles sleep during the plane ride?

Thought: _____

Information: _____

_____

Number Sentence: _____

Solution Sentence: _____

_____

Explain: _____

---

2. Lindsey earns $10 helping her mother with the garden. After buying a new T-shirt she has $3 left. How much money did Lindsey's new T-shirt cost?

Thought: _____

Information: _____

_____

Number Sentence: _____

Solution Sentence: _____

_____

Explain: _____

Solving Multiplication Word Problems with TINS

Multiplication word problems can be a blinding snowstorm. Set your compass for the long trail: TINS is here! Below are some key words that appear in multiplication word problems.

🔑 in all   🔑 product

🔑 groups   🔑 altogether

You may want to add others you know to the list. When you see a key multiplication word in a word problem circle it and put an xf above it. If you trace your steps you will find that the key words will help you lasso the right answer.

Example: Paulette's pencil box contains (9 hexagonal pencils.) Each pencil has (6 sides.) How many sides does Paulette have on her pencils (altogether?)

Thought: _____ x _____

Information: ___9 pencils, 6 sides on each___

Number Sentence: ___9 x 6 =___

Solution Sentence: ___There is a total of 54___

___sides on Paulette's pencils.___

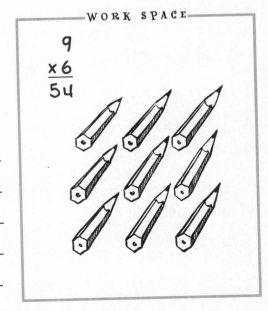

WORK SPACE

$$\begin{array}{r} 9 \\ \times 6 \\ \hline 54 \end{array}$$

Try It Out

Use TINS to solve these multiplication word problems. Remember to circle key words and draw pictures. Good Luck!

---

1. Samantha has 2 dogs. She gives each dog 2 bones. How many bones does Samantha give her dogs in all?

Thought: _____

Information: _____

_____

Number Sentence: _____

Solution Sentence: _____

_____

WORK SPACE

---

2. Cesar surprised his class by reporting that one earthworm can have 10 hearts. Cesar brought 3 earthworms to class today. How many hearts will Cesar report his earthworms have altogether?

Thought: _____

Information: _____

_____

Number Sentence: _____

Solution Sentence: _____

_____

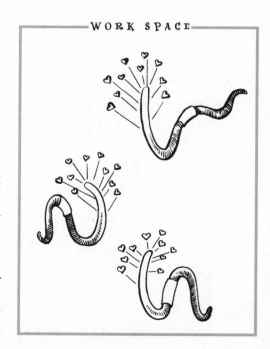

WORK SPACE

3. Melinda made necklaces for four friends. She gave each friend two necklaces. How many necklaces did Melinda make for all four friends?

T: _____

I: _____

_____

N: _____

S: _____

_____

W O R K   S P A C E

4. Quatina buys 7 bags of oranges. Each bag contains 2 oranges. How many oranges does Quatina buy in all?

T: _____

I: _____

_____

N: _____

S: _____

_____

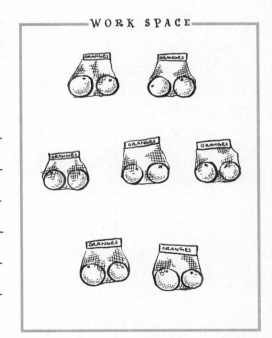

W O R K   S P A C E

5. Mrs. Winslow is preparing a box of fruit for her daughter Cynthia. She separates 4 rows of fruit with pink tissue paper. Each row contains 12 pieces of fruit. How many pieces of fruit will Cynthia receive?

T: _____

I: _____

_____

N: _____

S: _____

_____

WORK SPACE

6. Baby ducklings are born with three eyelids on each eye. If Opal has one duckling, how many eyelids are on Opal's duckling in all?

T: _____

I: _____

_____

N: _____

S: _____

_____

WORK SPACE

7. Mrs. Sabato announced that her pet flea can jump 7 inches in one leap. About how many inches will Mrs. Sabato's pet flea travel in 7 leaps?

T: _____

I: _____

_____

N: _____

S: _____

_____

WORK SPACE

8. Roosevelt carries 3 extra regulation hockey pucks every time he goes to the rink. Each puck is 1 inch thick. If Roosevelt stacks his pucks on the table, how many inches of hockey pucks will he have?

T: _____

I: _____

_____

N: _____

S: _____

_____

WORK SPACE

9. Chester Peacock fills the food containers on his farm three times in one day. Chester also fills the water dishes on Monday and Wednesday. After one week, how many times in all will Chester have filled the food containers?

T: _____

I: _____

_____

N: _____

S: _____

_____

WORK SPACE

10. Mr. McDaniel loves to read! He reads two books every day. How many books will he have read after three days?

T: _____

I: _____

_____

N: _____

S: _____

_____

WORK SPACE

On Your Own

Use TINS to solve these word problems. Remember circling key words and drawing pictures are helpful.

1. Seven students from Mrs. Bennett's class are playing flag football. Each student wears two flags. How many flags do all seven students wear?

Thought: _____

Information: _____

_____

Number Sentence: _____

Solution Sentence: _____

_____

WORK SPACE

2. It took Flossie 120 drops of water to fill her teaspoon. How many drops of water will Flossie need to fill 3 teaspoons?

Thought: _____

Information: _____

_____

Number Sentence: _____

Solution Sentence: _____

_____

WORK SPACE

3. Sarah selected 4 of her favorite shirts from her closet. Each shirt had 6 pink buttons and 2 pockets. How many buttons were on all 4 shirts?

T: _____

I: _____

_____

N: _____

S: _____

_____

WORK SPACE

4. Ellie has three cats. Each cat has four legs. How many legs are on all four cats altogether?

T: _____

I: _____

_____

N: _____

S: _____

_____

WORK SPACE

5. Anthony enjoys working on his math homework. He has seven rows of math problems to do. Each row has seven math problems. How many math problems does Anthony have for homework?

T: _____

I: _____

_____

N: _____

S: _____

_____

WORK SPACE

---

6. Almost all snowflakes have 6 sides. Edda Culpepper saw 6 snowflakes land on her roof. How many sides will Edda report were on these snowflakes altogether?

T: _____

I: _____

_____

N: _____

S: _____

_____

WORK SPACE

7. Jeremy ran 5 miles 3 days in a row. How many miles did Jeremy run in all?

T: _____

I: _____

_____

N: _____

S: _____

_____

WORK SPACE

8. Samantha saved her allowance for 3 weeks. Her allowance is $3 a week. How much money did Samantha save after 3 weeks?

T: _____

I: _____

_____

N: _____

S: _____

_____

WORK SPACE

9. Lavosha ate four bunches of grapes at snack time. Each bunch contained ten grapes. How many grapes did Lavosha eat in all?

T: _____

I: _____

_____

N: _____

S: _____

_____

WORK SPACE

10. Marley is printing out her report on her computer. The computer prints two pages of her report every minute. It takes Marley six minutes to print her report. How many pages will Marley's computer print in six minutes?

T: _____

I: _____

_____

N: _____

S: _____

_____

WORK SPACE

Take the Challenge I

Make a list of the key words you know for multiplication. Remember to look for these words as you solve each problem, circle them, and draw a picture. Take your time and remember REASONABLE answers are right answers. Think about each solution sentence and recheck it to make sure it makes sense!

1. Will and Todd built three birdhouses every day for three days. How many birdhouses did they build in all?

Thought: _____

Information: _____

_____

Number Sentence: _____

Solution Sentence: _____

_____

WORK SPACE

2. Olive's sea chest contains pirates, Vikings, dragons, and gold coins. In each of the 3 sections of her sea chest, Olive keeps 13 pirates each. How many pirates does Olive have in all?

Thought: _____

Information: _____

_____

Number Sentence: _____

Solution Sentence: _____

_____

WORK SPACE

3. Duval has five bags of golf balls. There are nine balls in each bag. How many golf balls does Duval have in all?

WORK SPACE

T: _____

I: _____

_____

N: _____

S: _____

_____

4. The gorilla and Mrs. Borge's house cat have one thing in common. Both animals sleep about 14 hours every day. After 1 week about how many hours will each animal have slept in all?

WORK SPACE

T: _____

I: _____

_____

N: _____

S: _____

_____

5. Fred has been scoring two goals during every soccer game. How many goals will Fred score in six soccer games if he continues his streak?

T: _____

I: _____

_____

N: _____

S: _____

_____

WORK SPACE

6. Lane brings cans of fruit drink to choir practice. He brings four boxes of fruit drink to every practice. Each box contains six cans. How many fruit drinks does Lane bring to one practice?

T: _____

I: _____

_____

N: _____

S: _____

_____

WORK SPACE

7. Tara loves to talk on the phone! If she talks on the phone for two hours every night for three nights, what is the total number of hours Tara will have talked on the phone?

T: _____

I: _____

_____

N: _____

S: _____

_____

WORK SPACE

---

8. The giant African snail can grow to be 1 foot long and can weigh about 1 pound. How many pounds would 22 African snails weigh altogether?

T: _____

I: _____

_____

N: _____

S: _____

_____

WORK SPACE

9. Marsha would like to buy her mother a birthday gift. She saves $4 a week for 5 weeks. How much money does Marsha save?

WORK SPACE

T: _____

I: _____

_____

N: _____

S: _____

_____

10. Egbert counted 12 inches in one foot. How many inches will Egbert count in 6 feet?

WORK SPACE

T: _____

I: _____

_____

N: _____

S: _____

_____

Take the Challenge II

Use TINS to solve these multiplication word problems. Remember to circle key words and draw pictures. Good Luck!

---

1. On a hot Saturday afternoon Patty and Dunn decide to sell slices of watermelon. Patty and Dunn each have ten pieces of watermelon to sell. If they both sell all their slices, how many will they sell altogether?

T: _____

I: _____

_____

N: _____

S: _____

_____

WORK SPACE

---

2. Three monkeys eat bananas. Each monkey eats six bananas. How many bananas do the monkeys eat in all?

T: _____

I: _____

_____

N: _____

S: _____

_____

WORK SPACE

3. There are five fans cooling off a very hot room. If each fan has three blades, how many blades are there in all?

WORK SPACE

T: _____

I: _____

_____

N: _____

S: _____

_____

4. Santiago is preparing to wash his laundry. He has four large bags of laundry to wash. Each bag of laundry contains four towels. How many towels will Santiago wash?

WORK SPACE

T: _____

I: _____

_____

N: _____

S: _____

_____

5. Renee travels to the beach two times during the summer. Each time she visits the beach she stays for three days. How many days does Renee spend at the beach in all?

T: _____

I: _____

_____

N: _____

S: _____

_____

WORK SPACE

6. The McDavid's have two windows in every room in their house. Their house has eight rooms. How many windows are in the McDavid's home?

T: _____

I: _____

_____

N: _____

S: _____

_____

WORK SPACE

7. Parnell knows that 1 giant clam can weigh 550 pounds. How many pounds will Parnell estimate 3 giant clams will weigh?

T: _____

I: _____

_____

N: _____

S: _____

_____

WORK SPACE

8. Elwanda believes a queen bee can lay as many as 3,000 eggs in a single day. How many eggs will she say a bee may lay in 3 days?

T: _____

I: _____

_____

N: _____

S: _____

_____

WORK SPACE

9. Herberto has counted 24 hours in one day. He will use this information to find the total number of hours there are in 5 days. What will his answer be?

WORK SPACE

T: _____

I: _____

_____

N: _____

S: _____

_____

10. In one year Clarice Treadwell's milking cow produces 6,000 quarts of milk. How many quarts of milk will Clarice expect her cow to produce in 2 years?

WORK SPACE

T: _____

I: _____

_____

N: _____

S: _____

_____

Write Your Own I

Try writing your own multiplication word problem. Make a question out of the information provided then use TINS to solve your problems. Remember to circle all key words and draw pictures. Challenge your friends to solve some of the problems your create. Happy problem writing!

Example: The oldest living animal is the giant leatherback turtle. This turtle weighs as much as a small 2-ton elephant.

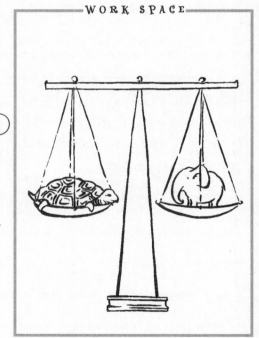

WORK SPACE

Question: The (giant leatherback turtle weighs as much as a small elephant.) If (one small elephant weighs 2 tons,) how many tons will (3 leatherback turtles) weigh (in all?)

Thought: ___x___

Information: each weighs 2 tons, 3 turtles

Number Sentence: 3 x 2 =

Solution Sentence: Three leatherback turtles will weigh 6 tons in all.

1. Great-great-grandfather bought 4 dozen eggs. There are 12 eggs in each dozen.

Question: _____

_____

_____

_____

Thought: _____

Information: _____

_____

Number Sentence: _____

Solution Sentence: _____

_____

WORK SPACE

---

2. Cleo buys two sandwiches every day. Five days have passed.

Question: _____

_____

_____

_____

T: _____

I: _____

_____

N: _____

S: _____

_____

WORK SPACE

3. Gabriella baked 5 pineapple upside-down cakes. They sold for $4.00 each.

Question: _____

_____

_____

_____

_____

T: _____

I: _____

_____

N: _____

S: _____

_____

WORK SPACE

---

4. Arnold camped for 2 weeks at the Last Ledge Lodge. There are 7 days in 1 week.

Question: _____

_____

_____

_____

_____

T: _____

I: _____

_____

N: _____

S: _____

_____

WORK SPACE

Write Your Own II

Write your own multiplication word problems. Remember to draw a picture, circle key words, and use TINS to solve each one. Happy problem writing!

---

1. _____

_____

_____

_____?

Thought: _____

Information: _____

_____

Number Sentence: _____

Solution Sentence: _____

_____

WORK SPACE

---

2. _____

_____

_____?

T: _____

I: _____

_____

N: _____

S: _____

_____

WORK SPACE

WORK SPACE

3. _____

_____

_____

_____?

T: _____

I: _____

_____

N: _____

S: _____

_____

WORK SPACE

4. _____

_____

_____

_____?

T: _____

I: _____

_____

N: _____

S: _____

_____

Solving Division Word Problems with TINS

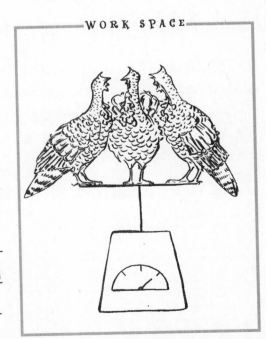

If TINS can help you with addition, subtraction, and multiplication word problems, then… you guessed it! TINS can keep you heading straight down the correct route, too. Check out these division key words.

- 🔑 each
- 🔑 quotient
- 🔑 equally
- 🔑 divide
- 🔑 separate

You may want to add others you know to the list. When you see a key division word in a problem circle it and put a ÷ above it. Think of yourself as a detective—the key words will give you a clue on own to solve the problem. Use the lines (TINS) to plug in your information from the word problem. Be careful, take your time, and have fun!

Example: Mr. Luna has (3 wild turkeys) in his pasture. They weigh a total of (180 pounds.) How many pounds will Mr. Luna's turkeys weigh (each?)

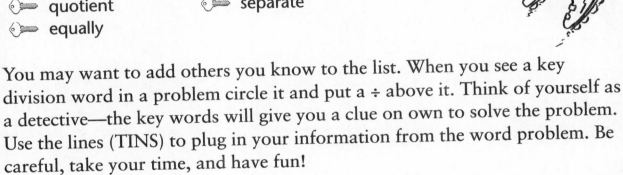
WORK SPACE

Thought: _____÷_____

Information: 3 turkeys, together weigh 180 pounds

Number Sentence: 180 ÷ 3 =

Solution Sentence: Mr. Luna's turkeys will weigh 60 pounds each.

Try It Out

Use TINS to solve these division word problems. Remember to circle key words and to cross out extra information. Also re-check each solution sentence to make sure it makes sense!

1. Francine buys twelve candles for Terri's and Tom's birthday cakes. She divides the candles equally between the twins' cakes. How many candles are on each cake?

Thought: _____

Information: _____

_____

Number Sentence: _____

Solution Sentence: _____

_____

WORK SPACE

2. Sandra and Lee want to divide a package of markers equally between themselves. One package contains ten markers. How many markers should each child receive?

T: _____

I: _____

_____

N: _____

S: _____

_____

WORK SPACE

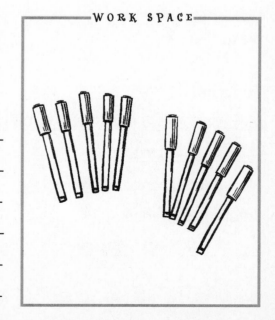

3. While Meg was on vacation she wrote eight letters to her two best friends. She wrote an equal number of letters to each friend. How many letters did Meg write to each friend?

WORK SPACE

T: _____

I: _____

_____

N: _____

S: _____

_____

4. Three ostriches can weigh 900 pounds. How many pounds will only one ostrich weigh?

WORK SPACE

T: _____

I: _____

_____

N: _____

S: _____

_____

5. Theresa and Wesley have twelve eggs. They want to divide the eggs equally. How many eggs will each person receive?

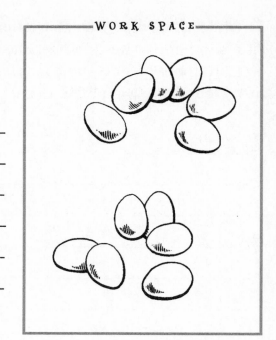

WORK SPACE

T: _____

I: _____

_____

N: _____

S: _____

_____

6. The giraffe at the Elwood Zoo sleeps a total of 20 minutes each night. The giraffe's sleep is split into 4 short naps each night. Find the number of minutes in each nap.

WORK SPACE

T: _____

I: _____

_____

N: _____

S: _____

_____

7. Theresa is putting books on three shelves in the library. She has nine books to divide equally among the shelves. How many books should Theresa put on each shelf?

T: _____

I: _____

_____

N: _____

S: _____

_____

WORK SPACE

8. After school Whitney wants to play with her friends. She also has homework to do. There are six hours before dinner. If Whitney divides her time equally, how much time will she spend playing with her friends and doing homework before dinner?

T: _____

I: _____

_____

N: _____

S: _____

_____

WORK SPACE

9. Hugo's elkhound weighs 5 times as much as his boxer. Hugo's elkhound weighs 140 pounds. How many pounds do you think Hugo's boxer weighs?

T: _____

I: _____

_____

N: _____

S: _____

_____

WORK SPACE

10. The antlers on 4 full-grown moose weigh a total of 240 pounds. How many pounds will the antlers on 1 moose weigh?

T: _____

I: _____

_____

N: _____

S: _____

_____

WORK SPACE

On Your Own

Please solve the following problems. Remember to circle key words, draw pictures, and use TINS to solve each problem. Have fun!

---

1. By midmorning Otis had collected 150 gallons of maple sap. Otis needs 50 gallons of sap to make 1 gallon of maple sugar. How many gallons of maple sugar does Otis have now?

Thought: _____

Information: _____

_____

Number Sentence: _____

Solution Sentence: _____

_____

WORK SPACE

---

2. On Monday Ms. McDaniel assigned eight pages of math homework that will be due on Wednesday. Hannah plans to do an equal number of pages over a two-day period. How many pages of math homework should Hannah do each night?

T: _____

I: _____

_____

N: _____

S: _____

WORK SPACE

3. Delicia has six hours to visit with her three best friends. She wants to spend an equal amount of time with each friend. How many hours will she be able to visit with each friend?

T: _____

I: _____

_____

N: _____

S: _____

_____

WORK SPACE

4. Ingrid wants to place her sweaters in two piles in her closet. She has sixteen sweaters. How many sweaters should she put in each pile?

T: _____

I: _____

_____

N: _____

S: _____

_____

WORK SPACE

5. Courtney has two books she wants to read. There is a total of eighteen pages in both books. The books have an equal number of pages. How many pages are in each book?

T: _____

I: _____

_____

N: _____

S: _____

_____

WORK SPACE

6. Bianca has twenty-six pieces of construction paper. She plans to divide the paper equally for two art projects. How many pieces of paper will Bianca use for each art project?

T: _____

I: _____

_____

N: _____

S: _____

_____

WORK SPACE

7. After baseball practice Joe is responsible for putting all the baseballs in three large bags. There is a total of twenty-one baseballs. If he puts an equal number of balls in each bag, how many baseballs will be put into each bag?

T: _____

I: _____

_____

N: _____

S: _____

_____

WORK SPACE

8. Twelve huge hippopotamuses spent all day submerged in the Zambesi River in Africa. At night the hippos separated into three packs to hunt for plants and grass to eat. How many hippos were in each pack?

T: _____

I: _____

_____

N: _____

S: _____

_____

WORK SPACE

9. During the week Owen sends fourteen e-mails to two friends. He sends an equal number of e-mails to each friend. How many e-mails does he send to each friend?

T: _____

I: _____

_____

N: _____

S: _____

_____

WORK SPACE

---

10. Montezuma, a South American Aztec king, made chocolate from his cacao bean plants. It was reported that Montezuma drank 350 cups of cocoa in 1 week. How many cups of cocoa did he drink in 1 day?

T: _____

I: _____

_____

N: _____

S: _____

_____

WORK SPACE

Take the Challenge

Circle key words, draw pictures, and use TINS to solve the following division problems. Happy problem solving!

---

1. Ted, Ed, Anthony, and Jerome went fishing. They caught a total of sixteen fish. If each boy caught an equal number of fish, how many fish did each person catch?

Thought: _____

Information: _____

_____

Number Sentence: _____

Solution Sentence: _____

_____

WORK SPACE

---

2. A large moving company has thirty-six boxes to deliver to six apartments. If they deliver an equal number of boxes to each apartment, how many boxes should each apartment receive?

T: _____

I: _____

_____

N: _____

S: _____

_____

WORK SPACE

3. There are forty-nine passenger cars on seven trains. How many passenger cars does each train have if each train has an equal amount of cars?

WORK SPACE

T: _____

I: _____

_____

N: _____

S: _____

_____

4. Cedric reports that one octopus has 8 arms and 3 hearts. If Cedric sees 24 octopus arms in a salt-water tank, how many octopuses will Cedric have seen?

WORK SPACE

T: _____

I: _____

_____

N: _____

S: _____

_____

5. Nana is getting ready for a party at her house. She has two large tables and twenty chairs. If she divides the chairs equally between the two tables, how many chairs will she put at each table?

T: _____

I: _____

_____

N: _____

S: _____

_____

WORK SPACE

6. During spring break Terrance completes twenty-five pages of his report over a five-day period. If he writes an equal number of pages each day, how many pages will he have written on each of the five days?

T: _____

I: _____

_____

N: _____

S: _____

_____

WORK SPACE

7. Mrs. Soto knows that 1 newborn polar bear cub weighs 15 pounds. The cubs at Cedar Zoo are reported to weigh a total of 45 pounds. How many cubs will Mrs. Soto find at Cedar Zoo?

T: _____

I: _____

_____

N: _____

S: _____

_____

WORK SPACE

8. Randell ordered a pizza containing twelve slices. He divided the slices equally between himself, his sister and his mother. How many pieces of pizza did each person receive?

T: _____

I: _____

_____

N: _____

S: _____

_____

WORK SPACE

9. Ralph took a shortcut to the Last Chance Lodge. Ralph divided his 12-mile trip equally between 3 stops. How many miles did Ralph travel before each stop?

T: _____

I: _____

_____

N: _____

S: _____

_____

WORK SPACE

10. Leo knows that 1 starfish in the Great Barrier Reef in Australia eats 32 feet of coral every 2 years. How many feet of coral will the starfish eat in only 1 year?

T: _____

I: _____

_____

N: _____

S: _____

_____

WORK SPACE

Write Your Own I

Try writing your own word problems. Make a question out of the information provided. Circle the key words, draw a picture, and use TINS to solve your problems. Challenge your friends to solve some of the problems you create!

Example: Tyrannosaurus Rex walked on 2 hind legs. Both legs had a total of 8 toes.

Question: _Tyrannosaurus Rex, the largest meat-eating dinosaur, walked on (2 hind legs.) These legs had a total of (8 toes.) How many toes were on (each) leg?_

Thought: _÷_

Information: _2 legs, 8 toes_

Number Sentence: _2 ÷ 8 =_

Solution Sentence: _Each Tyrannosaurus leg had 4 toes_

WORK SPACE

1. Harold's dune buggy uses 24 gallons of gas during a 2-day trip.

WORK SPACE

Question: _____

_____

_____

_____

_____

Thought: _____

Information: _____

Number Sentence: _____

Solution Sentence: _____

_____

2. Eight jumbo pretzels—four hungry people.

WORK SPACE

Question: _____

_____

_____

_____

_____

Thought: _____

Information: _____

Number Sentence: _____

Solution Sentence: _____

_____

3. Dora opened 6 drive-in restaurants. Half were closed Sunday.

Question: _____

_____

_____

_____

_____

T: _____

I: _____

_____

N: _____

S: _____

_____

WORK SPACE

4. Pine Bluff Trading Post employs ten people. Two employees work at each campsite.

Question: _____

_____

_____

_____

_____

T: _____

I: _____

_____

N: _____

S: _____

_____

WORK SPACE

Write Your Own II

Write your own division word problems. Remember to draw a picture, circle key words, and use TINS to solve them. Happy problem writing!

1. Question: _____

_____

_____

_____

_____?

Thought: _____

Information: _____

_____

Number Sentence: _____

Solution Sentence: _____

_____

WORK SPACE

2. Question: _____

_____

_____

_____?

T: _____

I: _____

_____

N: _____

S: _____

_____

WORK SPACE

3. Question: _____

_____

_____

_____

_____?

T: _____

I: _____

_____

N: _____

S: _____

_____

WORK SPACE

4. Question: _____

_____

_____

_____

_____?

T: _____

I: _____

_____

N: _____

S: _____

_____

WORK SPACE

Multiplication and Division Mixed Practice

Please circle key words, draw pictures, and use TINS to solve these problems. Re-check each solution sentence to make sure it makes sense!

---

1. Melanie has four envelopes. She places two stamps on each envelope. How many stamps will Melanie use in all?

Thought: _____

Information: _____

_____

Number Sentence: _____

Solution Sentence: _____

_____

WORK SPACE

---

2. Tyrone has twelve pens. He wants to divide his pens equally between his two school supply boxes. How many pens should he put in each box?

Thought: _____

Information: _____

_____

Number Sentence: _____

Solution Sentence: _____

_____

WORK SPACE

3. Virginia puts three picture frames each on four different shelves in her apartment. How many picture frames are on all four shelves?

Thought: _____

Information: _____

_____

Number Sentence: _____

Solution Sentence: _____

_____

WORK SPACE

4. Rex has a total of seventy-five cents. How many nickels will Rex receive for his seventy-five cents at the First Nickel Bank?

Thought: _____

Information: _____

_____

Number Sentence: _____

Solution Sentence: _____

_____

WORK SPACE

5. Three cats have kittens. Each cat has six kittens. How many kittens do all three cats have?

Thought: _____

Information: _____

_____

Number Sentence: _____

Solution Sentence: _____

_____

WORK SPACE

6. Florinda spent 14 days crossing the desert in her van. If there are 7 days in one week, how many weeks did Florinda's trip take in all?

T: _____

I: _____

_____

N: _____

S: _____

_____

WORK SPACE

7. Mrs. Moto has 36 tires in her inventory. How many sets of 4 tires can Mrs. Moto sell?

T: _____

I: _____

_____

N: _____

S: _____

_____

WORK SPACE

8. Vanessa draws nine happy faces on her paper. Each happy face has two eyes. How many eyes does Vanessa draw on her paper?

T: _____

I: _____

_____

N: _____

S: _____

_____

WORK SPACE

9. There are twelve students attending an after-school art class. There are four tables in the art room. If an equal number of students sit at each table, how many students will be at each table?

T: _____

I: _____

_____

N: _____

S: _____

_____

WORK SPACE

10. Lilly has four shirts hanging in her closet. Each shirt has three pockets. How many pockets are there on all four shirts?

T: _____

I: _____

_____

N: _____

S: _____

_____

WORK SPACE

11. Oliver bought a 40-pound bag of dog food for his dog Moose. If he feeds Moose 2 pounds of food each day, how many days will the food last?

WORK SPACE

T: _____

I: _____

_____

N: _____

S: _____

_____

12. There are 4 quarts of milk in 1 gallon of milk. How many quarts of milk are there in 3 gallons of milk?

WORK SPACE

T: _____

I: _____

_____

N: _____

S: _____

_____

13. Seven students attend a party. Each child receives a goody bag containing three toys in it. What is the total number of toys that all seven children receive?

T: _____

I: _____

_____

N: _____

S: _____

_____

WORK SPACE

---

14. Mrs. Moake has two grandchildren. She buys a total of four balloons for them while at the zoo. If each grandchild receives an equal number of balloons, how many balloons will each child receive?

T: _____

I: _____

_____

N: _____

S: _____

_____

WORK SPACE

15. Federico has just learned that there are 3 feet in 1 yard. How many feet will Frederico calculate there will be in 3 yards?

T: _____

I: _____

_____

N: _____

S: _____

_____

WORK SPACE

16. Brad has $20. He wants to divide the money equally between himself and his younger sister. How much money will each person receive?

T: _____

I: _____

_____

N: _____

S: _____

_____

WORK SPACE

17. There are twenty-one boxes of crayons in the Smiley Elementary School supply cabinet. If the boxes of crayons are divided equally between seven classes, how many boxes of crayons will each class receive?

T: _____

I: _____

_____

N: _____

S: _____

_____

18. Wilbur and his friend watched Wally climb up the steep side of Chimney Rock. It took Wally 2 hours. If 1 hour contains 60 minutes, how many minutes did it take Wally to reach the top of Chimney Rock?

T: _____

I: _____

_____

N: _____

S: _____

_____

19. Tyler has three pairs of tennis shoes. Each pair of shoes has two shoelaces. How many shoelaces are on all three pairs of shoes?

T: _____

I: _____

_____

N: _____

S: _____

_____

WORK SPACE

20. Six children begin their bicycle ride through Prospect Park. Each child rides a bike that has two wheels. How many wheels are on all six bicycles?

T: _____

I: _____

_____

N: _____

S: _____

_____

WORK SPACE

Final Mixed Review

Use TINS to solve these problems. Remember to circle key words and draw pictures. Be careful and take your time. Have fun!

---

1. Maggie's classroom has four computers. Each computer has two speakers. How many speakers are on all four computers?

Thought: _____

Information: _____

_____

Number Sentence: _____

Solution Sentence: _____

_____

> WORK SPACE

---

2. The class voted 26 to 13 to elect Donald W. Dibble class president. How many more votes did Donald receive than his opponent?

Thought: _____

Information: _____

_____

Number Sentence: _____

Solution Sentence: _____

_____

> WORK SPACE

3. Thirty people from El Paso wish to fly to Fort Worth. Each plane will hold six passengers. How many planes will be needed?

Thought: _____

Information: _____

_____

Number Sentence: _____

Solution Sentence: _____

_____

WORK SPACE

---

4. Ruby selected 12 silver buttons to attach to Colonel Plum's jacket. She remembers putting 8 brass buttons on the same jacket in June. How many buttons has Ruby sewn onto Colonel Plum's jacket in all?

Thought: _____

Information: _____

_____

Number Sentence: _____

Solution Sentence: _____

_____

WORK SPACE

5. While walking around the woodland and desert terrariums, Domingo counted 8 ferns and 11 cactus plants. How many plants did Domingo count altogether?

Thought: _____

Information: _____

_____

Number Sentence: _____

Solution Sentence: _____

_____

WORK SPACE

6. Two friends decide to play golf on Saturday. They take along four bags of golf balls. Each bag contains nine golf balls. How many golf balls do the friends take with them to play golf in all?

T: _____

I: _____

_____

N: _____

S: _____

_____

WORK SPACE

7. Yolanda is writing a twelve-page report for her history class. She decides to write an equal number of pages each day for three days. How many pages will Yolanda write each day?

T: _____

I: _____

_____

N: _____

S: _____

_____

8. The school store sells erasers. They have one box of orange erasers, one box of green erasers, and one box of purple erasers. There are ten erasers in each box. How many erasers does the school store have to sell?

T: _____

I: _____

_____

N: _____

S: _____

_____

9. There are thirty days in April. Nineteen of the days are sunny and the rest are rainy. How many rainy days are there in April?

T: _____

I: _____

_____

N: _____

S: _____

_____

WORK SPACE

---

10. Martina and Louis are taking a ten-hour train ride. They sleep for the first six hours of the train ride. How many hours do they have left on the train?

T: _____

I: _____

_____

N: _____

S: _____

_____

WORK SPACE

11. Three mothers take a walk. They each push a stroller. Each stroller has eight wheels. How many wheels are on all three strollers?

WORK SPACE

T: _____

I: _____

_____

N: _____

S: _____

_____

12. Mary bought eight picture frames. She frames five pictures so that one picture fits perfectly into one picture frame. How many picture frames does she have left?

WORK SPACE

T: _____

I: _____

_____

N: _____

S: _____

_____

13. Brenda has a CD case filled with CDs. The CD case has six shelves. Each shelf has five CDs. How many CDs does Brenda have in her CD case?

T: _____

I: _____

_____

N: _____

S: _____

_____

WORK SPACE

14. Matthew studied 2 hours on Monday, 3 hours on Tuesday, and 3 hours on Wednesday. He spent 6 hours at baseball practice. What is the total number of hours Matthew studied during the 3 days?

T: _____

I: _____

_____

N: _____

S: _____

_____

WORK SPACE

15. Mr. Flan is playing a math game with his students. He has fourteen spinners. He plans to give each of his seven students an equal number of spinners to play the game. How many spinners will each student receive?

WORK SPACE

T: _____

I: _____

_____

N: _____

S: _____

_____

16. Five children plan to be in a school play. There are thirty costumes for the play. Each child will wear an equal number of costumes during the play. How many costumes will each child wear during the play?

WORK SPACE

T: _____

I: _____

_____

N: _____

S: _____

_____

17. Head Chef Crum at Moon Lake Lodge is famous for his potatoes. Each year he prepares 3 tons of potatoes. About how many tons of potatoes will Chef Crum prepare in 4 years?

T: _____

I: _____

_____

N: _____

S: _____

_____

WORK SPACE

18. Quatina and Paul will share their computer at home. They are allowed to spend twenty-two hours using the computer during the week. If they divide these hours equally, how many hours can each person spend on the computer during the week?

T: _____

I: _____

_____

N: _____

S: _____

_____

WORK SPACE

19. There were six motorboats on the lake. Each boat has one engine. The sailboats all sail for three hours. What is the total number of engines on all six boats?

WORK SPACE

T: _____

I: _____

_____

N: _____

S: _____

_____

20. Students in Ms. Whittle's class signed up to work at the school carnival. Nineteen students sign up to work Saturday and seventeen students sign up to work the carnival on Sunday. How many students sign up to work the carnival in all?

WORK SPACE

T: _____

I: _____

_____

N: _____

S: _____

_____

21. Howie buys eighteen tickets for the fair. He has just enough tickets to take nine rides. If each ride costs an equal number of tickets, how many tickets will he use for each ride?

WORK SPACE

T: _____

I: _____

_____

N: _____

S: _____

_____

---

22. There are twelve months in a year. There are four seasons in a year. If each season has an equal number of months, how many months long is each season?

WORK SPACE

T: _____

I: _____

_____

N: _____

S: _____

_____

23. The ice on Holland Pond is 8 inches thick. Mabel knows that to skate on the pond the ice should be 5 inches thick. How many more inches thick is the Holland Pond ice?

T: _____

I: _____

_____

N: _____

S: _____

_____

WORK SPACE

24. Susan has eight baskets and forty baby bunnies. She wants to take a picture of the baskets with an equal number of bunnies in each basket. How many bunnies does Susan need to put in each basket?

T: _____

I: _____

_____

N: _____

S: _____

_____

WORK SPACE

25. Jason swims two hours a day every day for five days. What is the total number of hours Jason swims during the five days?

T: _____

I: _____

_____

N: _____

S: _____

_____

WORK SPACE

---

26. Marissa and her brother play fifteen games of table tennis while they are on vacation. They are on vacation for three days. If they play an equal number of games each day, how many games does Marissa play with her brother each day of vacation?

T: _____

I: _____

_____

N: _____

S: _____

_____

WORK SPACE

27. Lupe has six red notebooks, four yellow notebooks, and three black notebooks. How many yellow and red notebooks does Lupe have in all?

WORK SPACE

T: _____

I: _____

_____

N: _____

S: _____

_____

28. Melissa baby-sat for her three cousins for five hours Saturday night and six hours Sunday afternoon. What is the total number of hours Melissa baby-sat for her cousins?

WORK SPACE

T: _____

I: _____

_____

N: _____

S: _____

_____

29. In one load of laundry Thad counts seven shirts, six pairs of pants, eighteen socks, and three sweatshirts. How many socks and sweatshirts does Thad count?

WORK SPACE

T: _____

I: _____

_____

N: _____

S: _____

_____

30. Will brings his plants inside during the winter. He brings 14 plants inside. When the weather gets warmer he moves 8 plants outside. How many plants does Will still have inside?

WORK SPACE

T: _____

I: _____

_____

N: _____

S: _____

_____

31. Mother hamsters can produce one dozen babies in one month. Altogether how many baby hamsters could be produced in 3 months?

T: _____

I: _____

_____

N: _____

S: _____

_____

WORK SPACE

32. Four neighbors are playing a game with beans. They have a total of thirty-six beans. If they divide the beans equally, how many beans will each neighbor receive?

T: _____

I: _____

_____

N: _____

S: _____

_____

WORK SPACE

33. Salena has fifteen chores to do over the weekend. She finishes nine of her chores on Saturday. How many chores does Salena have left?

T: _____

I: _____

_____

N: _____

S: _____

_____

WORK SPACE

34. Between the pea patch on the right and the tomato patch on the left, Petula planted a patch of carrots. How many patches of vegetables did Petula plant in all?

T: _____

I: _____

_____

N: _____

S: _____

_____

WORK SPACE

35. Randy, Sandy, Mandy, and Candy are running in a relay race. The race is eight miles long. During the race each girl is going to run an equal distance and then pass a baton to the next runner. How many miles will each girl run?

WORK SPACE

T: _____

I: _____

_____

N: _____

S: _____

_____

36. Elm Farm Ollie was the first cow to fly in an airplane over Missouri. Halfway through the flight 2 parachutes were dropped over St. Louis. If each parachute held 8 containers of milk, how many containers of milk were dropped in all?

WORK SPACE

T: _____

I: _____

_____

N: _____

S: _____

_____

37. It is believed that the ancient elephant bird produced an egg big enough to make 1 omelet for 90 people. About how many omelets could 3 eggs produce?

T: _____

I: _____

_____

N: _____

S: _____

_____

WORK SPACE

38. Bebe knows that there are 60 seconds in 1 minute. How many seconds will Bebe expect to find in 4 minutes?

T: _____

I: _____

_____

N: _____

S: _____

_____

WORK SPACE

39. It took Stephen Crane 10 days to write his famous book *The Red Badge of Courage*. If he wrote 16 pages every day, how many pages are in Mr. Crane's book?

T: _____

I: _____

_____

N: _____

S: _____

_____

WORK SPACE

40. In South America, Arturo saw the world's largest water hog. It weighs 174 pounds. On his trip to Canada Arturo saw the famous beaver that weighs 87 pounds. How many more pounds did the South American rodent weigh?

T: _____

I: _____

_____

N: _____

S: _____

_____

WORK SPACE

41. One of the biggest pigs came from North Carolina and weighed 1,904 pounds. Don Castro lives in California and his pig weighs 180 pounds. How many pounds lighter is Don Castro's pig?

T: _____

I: _____

_____

N: _____

S: _____

_____

WORK SPACE

Write an addition, subtraction, multiplication, or division problem! Circle key words, draw a picture and solve it!

Word Problem: _____

_____

_____

_____

Thought: _____

Information: _____

_____

Number Sentence: _____

Solution Sentence: _____

_____

WORK SPACE

You can write the keywords that you know in each operation sign. Then cut out the signs and put them on your desk or in your math folder.

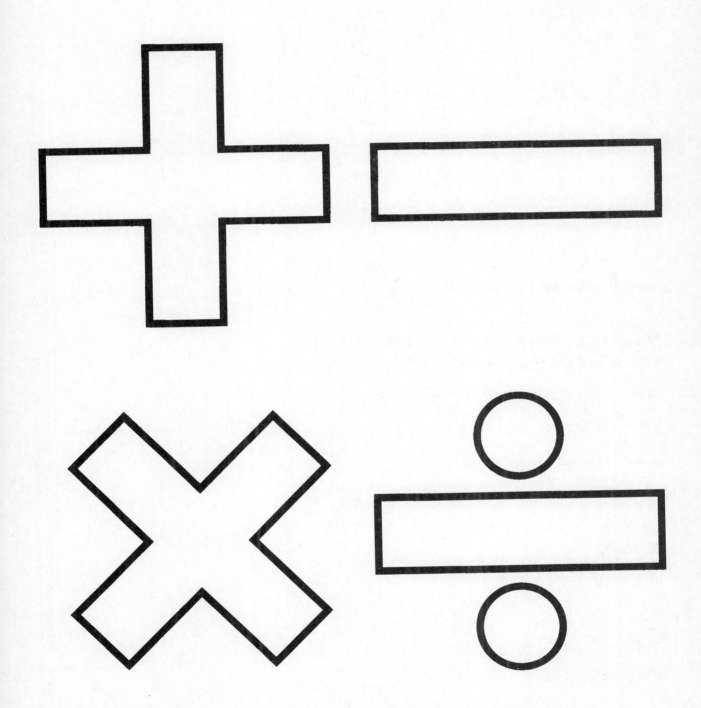